THE STORY OF THE THAMES BARRIER

Ken Wilson

Series Editor
SHEILA DUNN

The Story of the Thames Barrier

© Ken Wilson & The New Century Press Ltd · 1989

ISBN · 1 871826 00 4

First Published in 1984 by Lanthorn Publishing Ltd

PAPERBACK · ISBN · 0 947987 05 3
HARDBACK · ISBN · 0 947987 06 1

The New Century Press Limited
6 Grainger Road
Southend·on·Sea · Essex SS2 5BZ

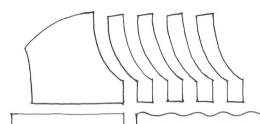

INTRODUCTION

MR ILLTYD HARRINGTON, JP.
THE RT. HON. THE CHAIRMAN
OF THE GREATER LONDON COUNCIL

The GLC's Thames Barrier, which was inaugurated by Her Majesty The Queen on 8th May 1984, is one of the great achievements of the twentieth century. Not only is it a marvellous piece of advanced engineering technology but it also provides an example of the way in which a large strategic authority can bring to fruition a scheme of such magnitude. It shows that political groups of all kinds can work together when the occasion demands.

Many members of this Council and staff from across a wide range of disciplines: engineers, architects, surveyors, accountants, administrators and many others, have been concerned with the project. Thousands of people from around the country, from Wilton in Wiltshire to Renfrew in Scotland, from Fareham in Hampshire to Darlington in County Durham and many other places have had a part to play in manufacturing and assembly, construction and commissioning of this great feat. And we must not forget the contribution of our Dutch friends, particularly at the early stages of construction.

We were not faced with a disaster which might have happened but one which, sooner or later, most certainly would have happened, and we are proud to have been responsible for bringing to completion this project which will protect Londoners for generations to come.

Illtyd Harrington

24 OCTOBER 1984

King Canute's celebrated encounter
 with the rising waves took place
 not on the seashore but on the
 north bank of the River Thames at
 a spot close to Westminster Abbey.

This clearly indicates that by the early
 years of the 11th century the river
 had become tidal. It was not always
 so. Over the past 2,000 years the
 high water level has risen by about
 4·2 metres (15 ft.) but gradual melting
 of the polar ice caps has caused the
 sea to rise relatively higher.

Sixty five years after Canute's death
 there was the first surviving report
 of flooding in London. The Anglo
 Saxon chronicle for 1099 records :

" On the Festival of St Martin (now on
 11 November) the sea flood sprang
 up to such a height and did so much
 harm as no man remembered that it
 did before and this was the first
 day of the new moon. "

Another occurred on the same day in 1236 :

"...which caused the marshes about
 Woolwich to be all at sea wherein
 boats and other vessels were carried
 in the stream. In the great Palace
 of Westminster men did row with
 wherries in the midst of the Hall."

Canada

GULF STREAM

LABRADOR CURRENT

Europe

ATLANTIC OCEAN

Africa

The main flood danger comes from surge tides down the North Sea. These originate off the coast of Canada, where the warm water of the Gulf Stream meets the cold Labrador Current. This creates a zone of low atmospheric pressure which raises the level of the sea about 300 mm (1 ft) over an area approximately 1,000 miles in diameter. This hump of water moves across the Atlantic at a speed of 50 to 60 miles per hour.

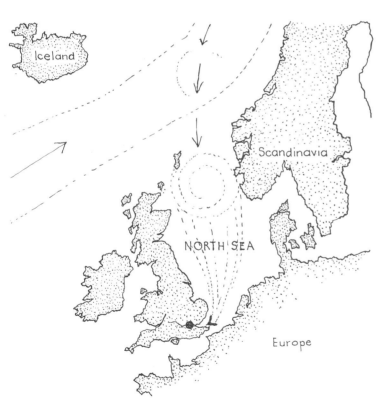

Iceland

Scandinavia

NORTH SEA

Europe

Usually these depressions move in a north easterly direction between Iceland and Scandinavia and do no damage, but occasionally they meet a strong southerly wind and are forced into the North Sea.

This sends millions of tons of extra water into the Thames Estuary and up the river, producing tides 3 metres (10 ft) higher than normal.

At the time Charles Dickens was writing, much of the area to the east of Woolwich was marshland. This was constantly flooded whenever tides were high but as there were no inhabitants it did not matter. This overflowing served as a safety factor for Central London. The land was progressively reclaimed during the 19th century, first by the building of dykes and later flood walls along the banks. Incoming tides were then confined and this raised the level, greatly increasing the danger upriver in the built-up areas of the capital.

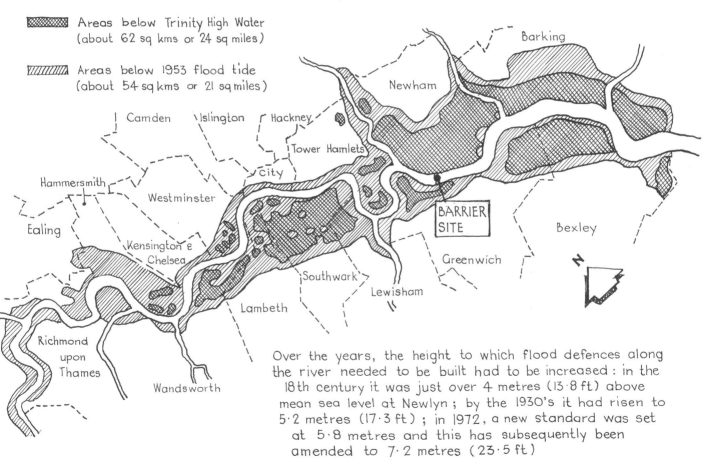

Areas below Trinity High Water (about 62 sq kms or 24 sq miles)

Areas below 1953 flood tide (about 54 sq kms or 21 sq miles)

Over the years, the height to which flood defences along the river needed to be built had to be increased: in the 18th century it was just over 4 metres (13·8 ft) above mean sea level at Newlyn; by the 1930's it had risen to 5·2 metres (17·3 ft); in 1972, a new standard was set at 5·8 metres and this has subsequently been amended to 7·2 metres (23·5 ft)

By the year 100 AD, sixty years after the Roman occupation of Britain, Londinium had become the principal port and administrative capital of the new colony. It developed on the north bank of the river on what is now the square mile of the City of London. The settlement was the focal point of the great road system. Trade flourished and the river was busy with shipping.

A bridge was built, close to the site of the present London Bridge, This was very convenient for pedestrian and vehicular traffic but it prohibited the passage of larger ships and they began to unload and take on cargoes down-river of the bridge, establishing the docks area in the East End of the City.

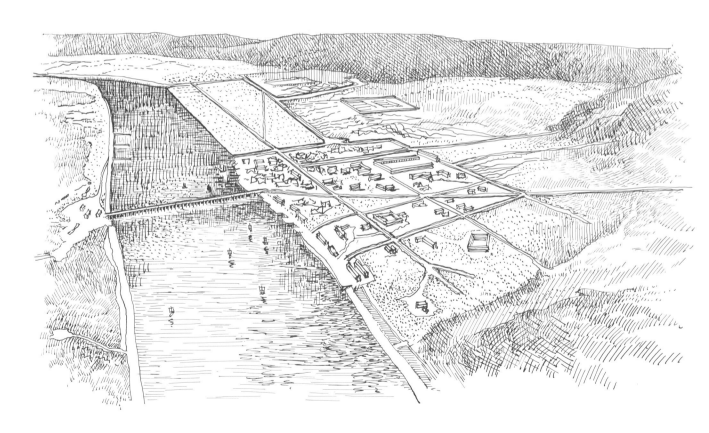

In the 12th century a new London Bridge was built of stone to replace the earlier timber structure. The arch spans were small and the piers wide because of limitations in construction methods. This restricted the flow and accelerated the velocity causing the river bed to be washed away in the openings. The piers were undermined by this action and to protect them the openings were given floors, called aprons, made of heavy timber beams. The piers were surrounded by piling to give extra support.

The bridge had the effect of calming the water upstream and during the next four centuries river traffic greatly increased as it became the main commuter route.

There was such a volume of potential customers on the bridge that it was widened by the addition of shops, with houses over, on both sides. This required more support for the piers, which led to a further increase in the speed of flow and "Shooting the Bridge" added excitement to the boat journey.

It was now totally impossible for ships of any size to pass beyond this point and this consolidated the commercial port's position downriver of London Bridge in what came to be called the Pool.

Samuel Pepys, who was a regular traveller on the river, recorded in his diary on 7 December 1663 :

" I hear there was last night the greatest tide that ever was remembered in England to have been in this river: all White Hall having been drowned."

The waters must have subsided quickly because he went walking there on the following day.

This and previous incidents hundreds of years earlier were the result of surge tides in the North Sea, each attaining a new height and overflowing what formerly had been safe defences.

During the 18th and 19th centuries the Port of London vastly increased. The advantages of loading and unloading vessels which floated at a constant level, instead of rising and falling with the tide, led to the construction of the huge dock systems with water impounded in basins with locks to allow ships to pass in and out.

St Katharine, London, Surrey, Millwall and the two India Docks were all built between 1802 and 1868; the much larger Royal Docks between 1855 and 1921.

Enormous demands for dock labour resulted in a rapid spread of new building along the banks into the old marshlands. These were drained but their low level made them liable to flooding.

A general increase in population added to the demand for space. There were only 958,000 inhabitants in London at the time of the first census in 1801. Forty years later this had doubled and by the turn of the century it had doubled again.

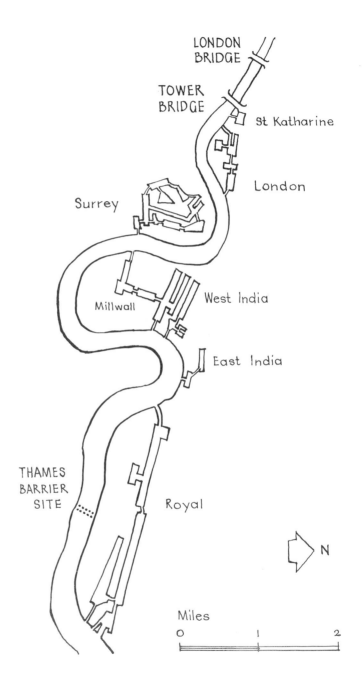

7

A disaster was caused in 1953 by a surge tide which rose only 1·2 metres (3·7 ft) above the high spring tide level at London Bridge. Much of the East Coast was affected. Canvey Island suffered very badly. Over 300 people were drowned. About 64,600 hectares (160,000 acres) of farmland was covered in saltwater and required over 100,000 tons of gypsum to restore it to productivity. The water reached parapet level in some parts of Central London. Had it gone over, damage would have been reckonable in millions of pounds. 1,200,000 people lived in the threatened area in 350,000 dwellings. The Underground would have been out of action for a year, water supplies would have been polluted and the entire economic activity of the capital severely disrupted.

At the end of April, the Government appointed a Departmental Commitee to examine the dangers and make recommendations.

The Chairman was Lord Waverley, better known as Sir John Anderson. He was Home Secretary at the onset of World War II and became generally well-known for the air raid shelter which bore his name.
Such was his reputation that he was Winston Churchill's nominee to take over as Prime Minister should anything happen to himself or his Deputy, Anthony Eden.

At the time of his appointment to the Commitee chairmanship he was 68 years old, an acknowledged expert on shipping and Chairman of the Port of London Authority.

The Waverley Committee reported within a year. It reviewed the available knowledge on the natural phenomena and concluded that the dangers were real. Further detailed study was recommended, with a view to devising an early warning system. It was considered that a physical structure of some kind was required across the river, but the type and siting were outside the Committee's terms of reference.

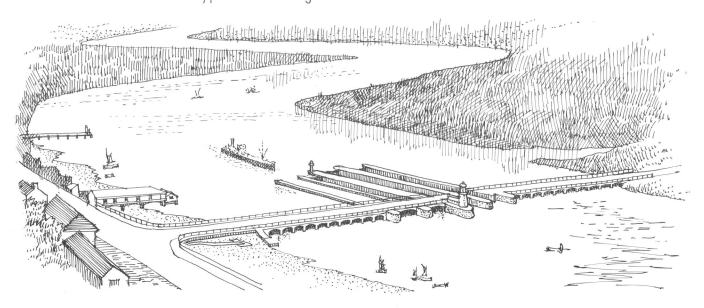

In 1907 a scheme was prepared for a barrage to be built at Gravesend. The idea was not new, in the 19th century there had been a proposal to build a barrage downstream of the then existing docks with a view to making the river calmer and slower-flowing, as it had been above London Bridge in Tudor times.

Locks were necessary to allow the passage of shipping and even with the amount of traffic at the time, this would have created an enormous bottleneck. Another problem which was not foreseen was that the slowing down of the current would have caused the silt to build up, gradually clogging the banks and the entrances to the docks.

The barrage principle was considered again during the 1930's but discarded due to its vulnerability to bombing. Damage to the lock could bring the entire port to a standstill.

It was Alan Price, a Port of London engineer, who first thought of a barrier to solve
The Thames's flooding problem.

The basic difference between a barrage and a barrier is that the former works
rather like a wier and is in position all the time, the latter only when required.
A barrage fundamentally alters the natural behaviour of the river – limiting tidal
changes above it, slowing the current, affecting the siltation and the balance.
A barrier does none of these things.

BARRAGE
Lift gates housed in permanent base.

BARRIER
Rising gates parked horizontally

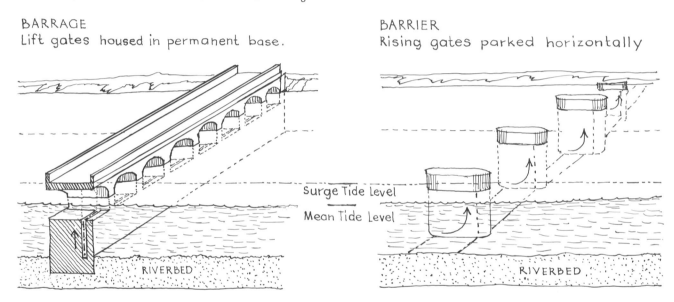

Surge Tide Level

Mean Tide Level

RIVERBED

RIVERBED

In 1954, Price was carrying out a study of the siltation of the Thames Estuary,
using a scale model of the river built at the Royal Docks. He cut a piece of
hardboard to fit the shape of the river bed at Long Reach then simulated the
effects of a surge tide. It was clear from his experiments that it was a feasible
proposition and that there would be no harmful reactions. What had been feared
was that, if an obstruction was placed in the path of an incoming tide, there
would be a reflected wave that would "bounce" back from it. The inhabitants
of Canvey Island were particularly concerned with the possibility of this causing
even higher tides in their vicinity. The results demonstrated that this would not
happen. These findings were later confirmed mathematically by Joe Otter, a partner
in the consultant engineering practice which designed the Barrier.

Soon after the Waverley Commitee had reported in 1954, the Thames Technical Panel took over responsibility. The Panel included the Chief Engineers from the various local authorities fronting the river, Government Departments concerned and other interests affected. They were asked to make a survey of existing flood defences, give estimates of the cost of raising them, consider some form of structure across the river and advise on the appointment of consultants.

The barrage proposal was looked at again, but discarded as impractical. A barrier of some kind was the preferred solution.

A new defence level was fixed at 1.6 metres (6.0 ft) above that reached by the 1953 flood. This necessitated many miles of river bank and walling being raised but created the opportunity to provide some attractive riverside walks.

A site was selected for the barrier at Long Reach, some 5 miles upriver from the 1907 barrage at Gravesend. At Long Reach the river is 696.3 metres (2,300 ft) wide and the bed is 12.9 metres (42.5 ft) below mean sea level. At the new defence level the barrier would have to retain a water depth of 19·6 metres (65 ft)

Two firms of consulting engineers were appointed: Rendel, Palmer & Tritton who had previously been responsible for most of London Docks and Sir Bruce White, Wolfe Barry & Partners. Sir Bruce had been knighted for his work on the Mulberry Harbour used for the D-Day landings and Wolfe Barry was a former Resident Engineer of Tower Bridge.

To allow the passage of ocean-going ships, the Port of London Authority asked for two openings, each 157.5 metres (500 ft) wide with 61 metres (200 ft) clear height.

The first proposal was for a lifting bridge, incorporating barrier gates which could be lowered on to the river bed when the bridge was in the down position.

A lifting bridge barrier would have been an enormous structure, towering about 91.5 metres (300 ft) into the air. There were planning and environmental objections.

A swing bridge barrier was more in line with existing engineering practice. There were many examples of this type – though none with such large spans. Of the three principles considered, the swing movement was the most conventional, economical and speediest in operation.

The third proposal put forward was for a retractable bridge barrier. Nothing of this size had ever been built before. All kinds of problems were foreseeable

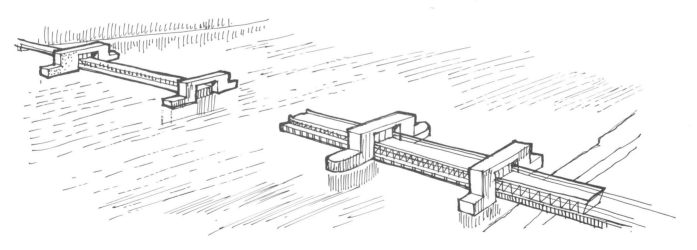

All three solutions seemed to have fundamental drawbacks : with the lift, it was height ; the swing required more river space ; the retractable, more on-shore land.

Years of frustrating controversy passed
and the whole concept needed its
supporters.

Possibly the best-known to the
general public was A.P. (later Sir Alan)
Herbert. Author of many books and
some musical comedies, he was also a
regular contributor to Punch as A.P.
Haddock. A celebrated wit, he missed
no opportunity to debunk people and
institutions he considered "puffed up".
First World War experience in the
Royal Navy and with the Thames
Emergency Service in the Second gave
him a deep love of boats and the River
of which he was a conservator. He was
looked upon as Old Father Thames himself.

Others who used their influence and made a significant contribution to keeping
the project alive were : Lord Kennet, formerly Parliamentary Under Secretary
at the Department of the Environment, more widely known as Wayland Young a
writer on social questions ; Eldon Griffiths, Lord Kennet's successor at the
Department, a journalist who made many appearances on television and the
Assistant Secretary with special responsibility for the barrier scheme, Richard Adams,
later to achieve fame as the author of "Watership Down".

Since merchant shipping began goods had been carried on deck or in the holds of vessels - items having to be stowed, usually by being manhandled into position. By the mid 1960's the entire method of conveying cargoes by sea was radically changing. The introduction of strongly built containers meant that these could be packed, normally at the place where the goods were produced, and hoisted by crane into specially designed ships. These changes required more open space and the centre for cargo handling moved from the older London docks to Tilbury.

St Katharine's was the first to close. Built by Thomas Telford, engineer of the Caledonian Canal and the Menai Bridge, with buildings designed by Philip Hardwick, the architect of Euston Station, it was opened in 1828. The Dock has been preserved and is now a public leisure area.

Other changes had taken place while the barrier project was under discussion. New loading jetties had been built and Long Reach was now required as a turning space for ships an was no longer available as a site. A new location for the barrier was suggested at Crayfordness. This was on a bend of the river and in view of navigational difficulties a clear opening of 424.2 metres (1,400 ft) was required by the Port Authority.

The Consulting Engineers said they could design to this requirement but it was "at the limit of technology". At the time there was no comparable parallel and completely new principles of design would have to be evolved without the benefit of previous practical experience with similar structures.

A single opening of this size ruled out the use of either a lift or swing bridge barrier. Both submitted designs were based on retractable bridge systems.

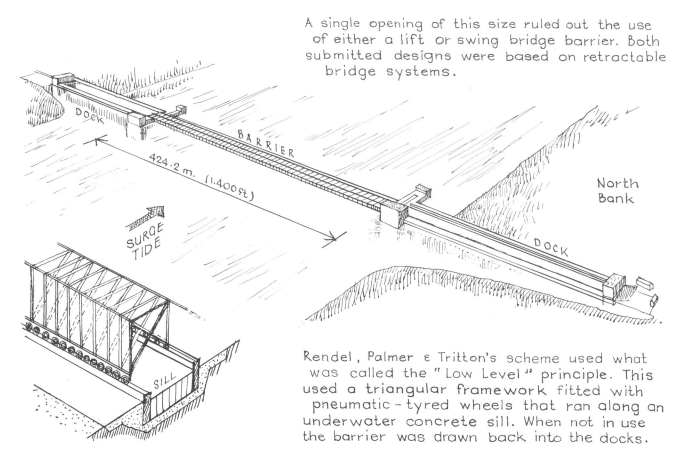

Rendel, Palmer & Tritton's scheme used what was called the "Low Level" principle. This used a triangular framework fitted with pneumatic-tyred wheels that ran along an underwater concrete sill. When not in use the barrier was drawn back into the docks.

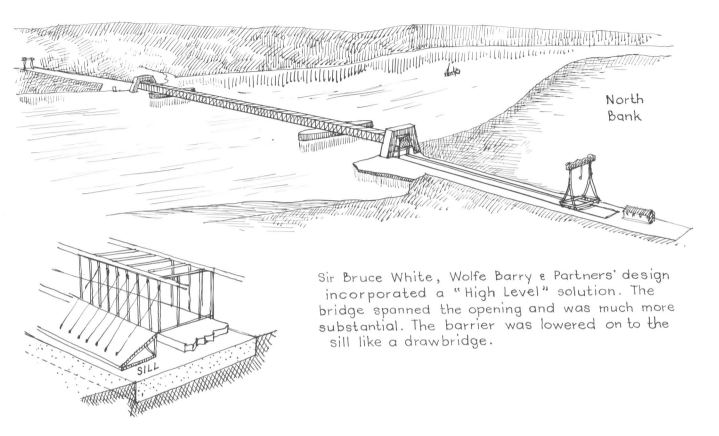

North Bank

Sir Bruce White, Wolfe Barry & Partners' design incorporated a "High Level" solution. The bridge spanned the opening and was much more substantial. The barrier was lowered on to the sill like a drawbridge.

SILL

Estimated costs for both these schemes were far in excess of the £15 - £17½ million for the Long Reach proposals. The Low Level design for Crayfordness was expected to cost £24 million, the High Level £42 million. When these were received on the last day of 1965, they were considered to be totally unacceptable figures – regardless of the current assessment of potential damage should flooding occur being in the region of £2,000 million.

In April of that year, the London Government Act had come into force which created the Greater London Council, a body with regional powers over all the affected areas, with its own highly competent executive, engineering and architectural staff.

The Government wanted to have another look at the whole concept and their Principal Scientific Adviser, Sir Solly Zuckerman (later Lord Zuckerman) recommended an independent report by a high ranking scientist of Nobel Prize calibre.

Professor Hermann Bondi FRS FRAS was the man chosen. He was an astronomer with an impressive list of top scientific appointments behind him and was Professor of Mathematics at King's College, London University.

He studied the entire question afresh and reaffirmed the need to take defensive measures — there were many people who thought it might never happen. Again the barrage principle was considered and rejected. New negotiations with the Port of London Authority produced agreement on much smaller openings if the barrier was sited above the entrance to the Royal Docks.

In May 1970 the Greater London Council was asked to undertake responsibility for the whole flood prevention scheme.

After investigating other locations the Woolwich site was finally chosen.

Professor Bondi's report was accepted. Government approval was obtained for the expenditure and the necessary statutory powers were granted.

The Council appointed Rendel, Palmer & Tritton as Consulting Engineers for the design and construction supervision of the Thames Barrier.

At Christmas of that year Charles Draper, a member of the design team, was turning on a gas fire at home when he realised that the way a gas tap works would form a suitable basis for the Barrier gates. He told the team and they developed it into the design.

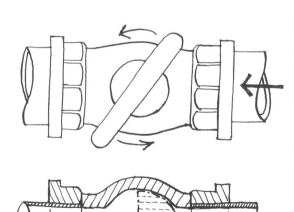

This became known as the **Rising Sector Gate** and it had enormous advantages over any other form : the weight and span problems of lift, swing or retractable bridges were avoided; the deep underwater excavations necessary for any kind of falling gate were not involved and there were many other ways in which it was superior, particularly in the manner of construction and maintenance.

The gates rotate on metal discs fitted to the piers. A reinforced concrete sill on the river bed provides a protective parking place for the gates, when in the down position, and an edge to close against when up.

Rising Sector gates operate in four main positions :

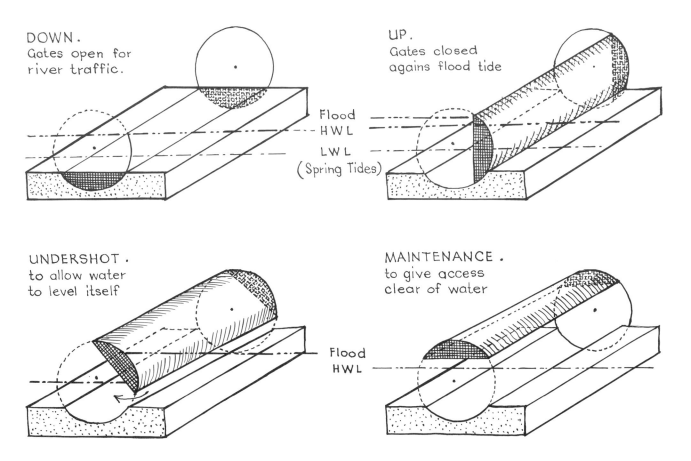

DOWN.
Gates open for
river traffic.

Flood
HWL

LWL
(Spring Tides)

UP.
Gates closed
agains flood tide

UNDERSHOT.
to allow water
to level itself

Flood
HWL

MAINTENANCE.
to give access
clear of water

As ships using this part of the river would be smaller, the openings in the Barrier need be no larger than the centre section of Tower Bridge which is 60·9 metres (200 ft).

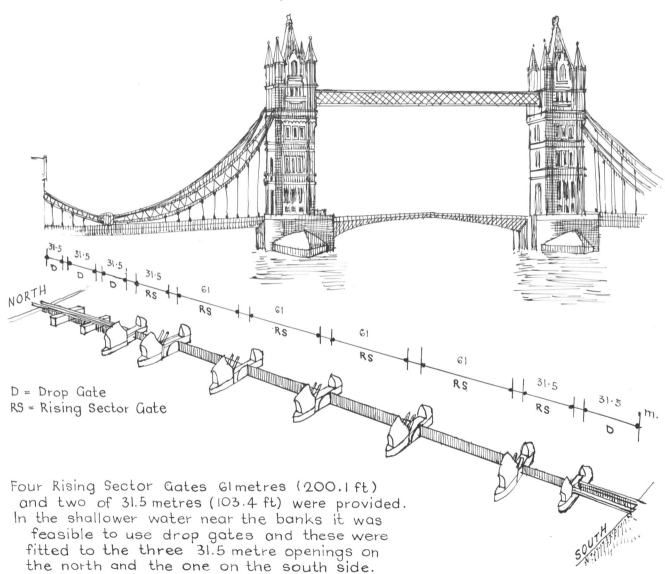

D = Drop Gate
RS = Rising Sector Gate

Four Rising Sector Gates 61 metres (200.1 ft) and two of 31.5 metres (103.4 ft) were provided. In the shallower water near the banks it was feasible to use drop gates and these were fitted to the three 31.5 metre openings on the north and the one on the south side.

To enable the piers to be built, coffer dams had to be placed round each position. These are made by driving sheet piles (strong steel corrugated strips interlocking to form watertight boxing) down into the solid chalk about 16 metres (52.8 ft) below the river bed.

While the water was still inside the dams, divers fixed steel joists to give support to the walls, to resist the pressure of the river when they are emptied. The divers worked in shifts and 250 were employed during the contract period. They had to work in zero visibility conditions. It was cold, heavy and dangerous work.

The water was pumped out and excavations for the concrete foundations went into the chalk another 15 metres (49.5 ft). The dams were deep enough to take six London buses on top of each other.

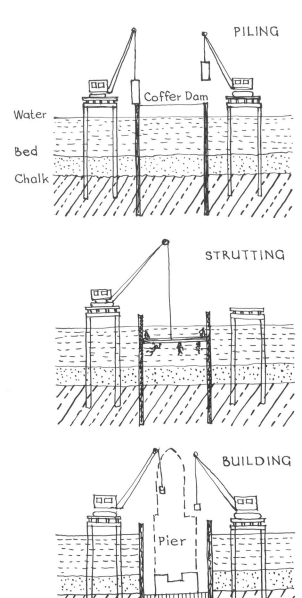

A temporary dry dock was constructed on the
north bank in which to manufacture the sills.
Sheet piling was again used to form three walls
jutting out into the water. After these were in
place, the area was pumped dry, the silt removed
and a work floor of concrete slabs was laid.
The larger sills were 60 metres (196.8 ft) long
and 27 metres (91.6 ft) wide, the smaller 31 metres
(101.6 ft) by 20 metres (65.6 ft) and the dock
was big enough to enable two of each to be
made at the same time in conditions similar
to a normal building site.

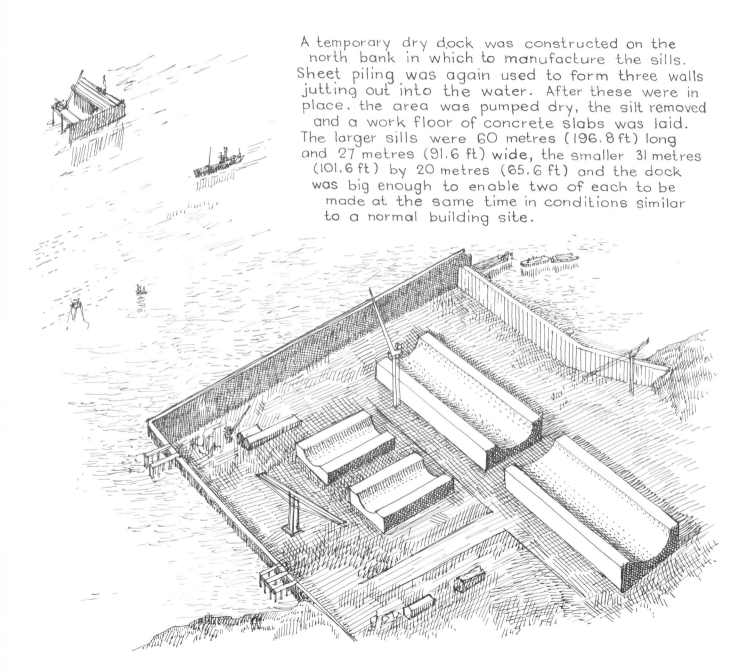

When located, the sills were flooded and sunk into position, with special jacks and cables to guide them and offset the pull of the current.

After completion of the sills, the dock was refilled with water and the walls were removed.

The larger sills weighed about 10,000 tonnes (9,842 tons) and the smaller 3,500 tonnes (3,444 tons) but were designed to float – air compartments were formed within the shape and temporary ends were fitted to increase buoyancy.

Tugs towed them into position between the piers. With only 100 mm (4 in) clearance it was one of the most critical jobs.

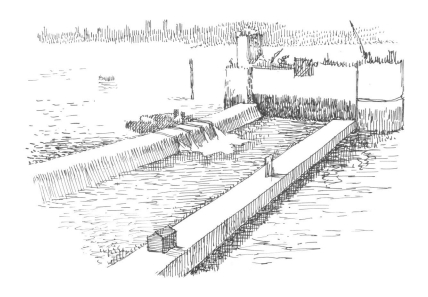

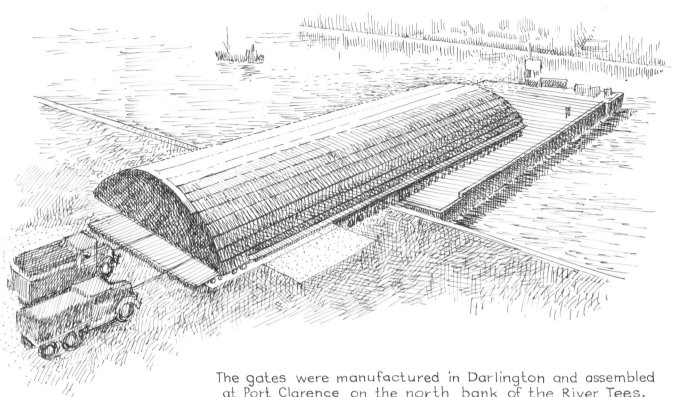

The gates were manufactured in Darlington and assembled at Port Clarence on the north bank of the River Tees, about 20 miles away. The large gates weighed 1,500 tonnes (1476.3 tons) and the maximum permitted sag when they were lifted was 25 mm (1 in).

Each one was jacked up and six bogeys, with 100 wheels on each, were moved underneath. Then they were rolled on to special barges. These had ballast tanks filled with water and as the load transferred from shore to ship some of these were pumped out to correct the tilt. Two heavy vehicles were attached to ensure that the load did not run away.

The barges carried the gates on the 300 mile voyage down the North Sea and up the Thames to the site.

The first gate was placed in position on 14 December 1981.

Two floating cranes picked one of the 61 metre units off its barge, carried it between piers 7 and 8 – the first wide opening off the south bank – and hoisted it high in the air. A blizzard then set in and it was not advisable to proceed with the fixing. Shortly after 7 a.m. the weather improved, work was resumed and by lunchtime the operation was completed.

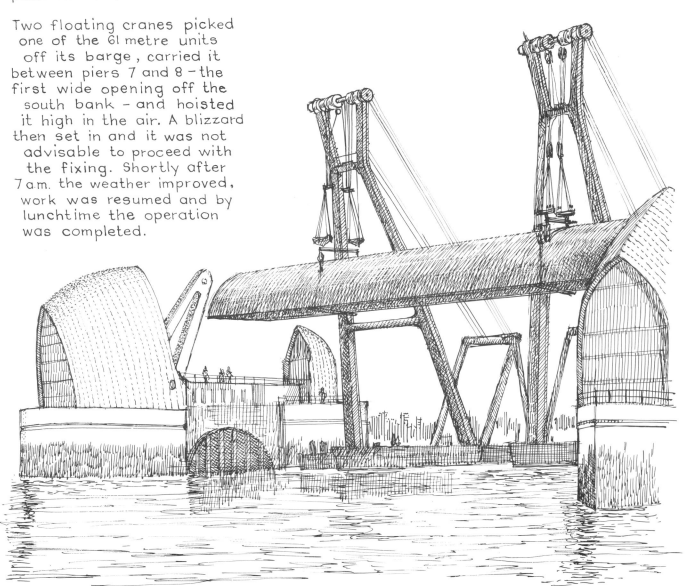

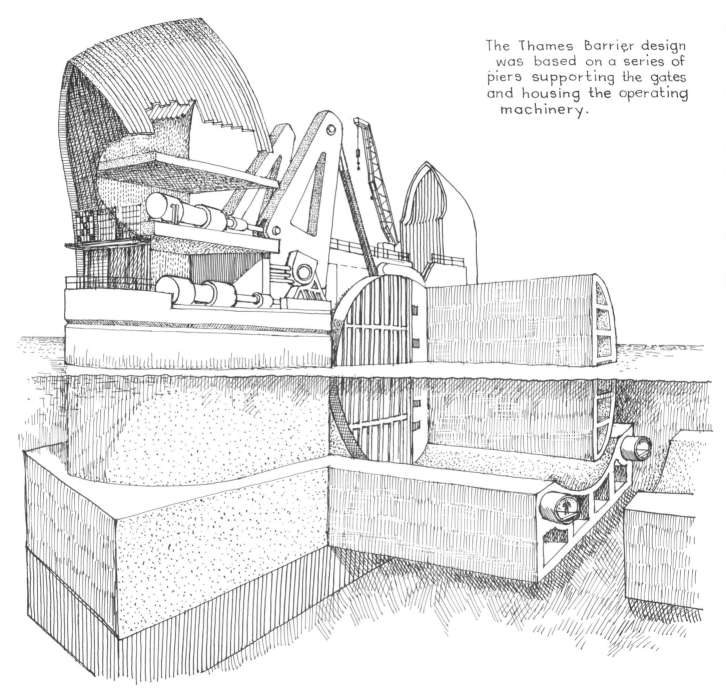

The Thames Barrier design was based on a series of piers supporting the gates and housing the operating machinery.

Reversible hydraulic rams were selected
as the best method of moving the gates.
These work in pairs which are coupled
to pivoted rocker arms joined to the
gate discs to give the four positions.

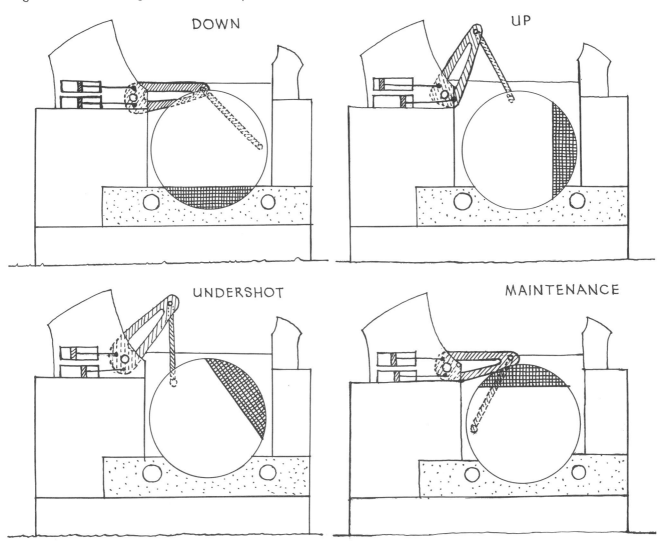

DOWN

UP

UNDERSHOT

MAINTENANCE

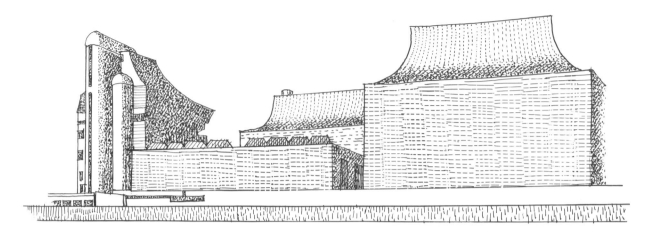

On-shore buildings and the roofs over the machinery on the piers were designed by
   the GLC's own architects. Timber was used to create the imaginative shapes,
inspired by a ship bow. The covering of stainless steel was fixed in narrow strips
 to enable the two-way curves to be followed. A weathertight joint was formed
  between the strips by turning up one edge and folding the next one over it. The
shape of the pier hoods required them to be constructed from the lower to the
upper edge. This was not a problem for a right handed workman on one side, but
  he would have needed to work upside down on the other, so left handed men were
   specially recruited.

Inside the Control Tower, weather and tidal conditions are constantly monitored. The decision to close the Barrier would be based on the East Coast Storm Tide Warning System based at Bracknell which gives information on dangerously high water levels which is gathered by weather ships in the Atlantic, oil rigs in the North Sea and on-shore recorders as far away as Stornaway in the Hebrides. Ominous conditions can be forecast at least 12 hours ahead. Action at the Barrier would be taken about one hour after low tide, fully four hours before an incoming surge tide could reach this point. The gates operate in 30 minutes.

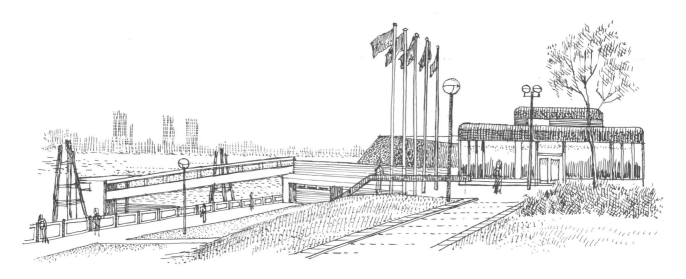

The Thames Barrier is unique and people from all over the world visit this achievement of modern technology and engineering.

On the south bank, adjacent to the Control Tower, The Barrier Centre is a permanent feature. Bright and cheerful buildings house exhibitions, audio-visual displays and a shop. The restaurant overlooks the river and boat trips round the Barrier leave from the pier.

THE THAMES BARRIER
WAS OFFICIALLY OPENED BY
HER MAJESTY THE QUEEN
ON THE 8th OF MAY 1984

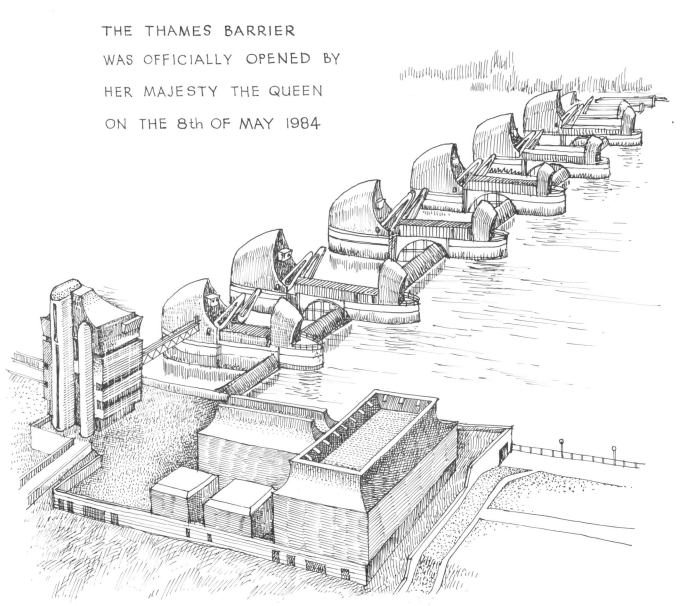

The final cost of the whole flood prevention scheme
was £550 million of which the Barrier cost £450 million.

Acknowledgements

My thanks for assistance to :

PETER BOSWORTH BSc FIPM FITD
Thames Recreation Development Officer.

DAVID WHITFIELD

STAFF OF THE THAMES BARRIER
VISITORS CENTRE

Published sources :

GLC BARRIER
Public Relations Branch.
Greater London Council · 1984

THE THAMES BARRIER
Stuart Gilbert and Ray Horner.
Thomas Telford Limited · 1984

LONDON
Geoffrey Trease
Thames and Hudson · 1975

HISTORY OF ENGLAND
G. M. Trevelyan OM
Longman · 1973

Various newspaper reports
and magazine articles.